A Midsummer Night's Dream

For John and Mary

Assistant editors:
Andrew Greaves
Victoria Gemmell

Cover design: Simon Hadlow, DP Press, St Julians, Sevenoaks, Kent, TN15 ORX

Series title: Comic Book Shakespeare: A Midsummer Night's Dream

Published by Timber Frame Publications Ltd, 2005

Printed in Portugal by Grafias SA

Distributed by: DP Press, St Julians, Sevenoaks, Kent, TN15 ORX
            Tel: 01732 458541 Fax: 01732 458162

Other titles also available:

Macbeth

Twelfth Night

Romeo and Juliet

Henry V

Each with an accompanying teacher's book

Visit our website at: www.shakespearecomics.com

ISBN A Midsummer Night's Dream Comic Book 0-9544325-8-4

British Library Cataloguing in Publication Data. A CIP catalogue record for this book is available from the British Library.

Comic Book
Shakespeare

A Midsummer
Night's Dream

by

William
Shakespeare

**Edited, with a
modern English
translation
and illustrated
by**

Simon Greaves

TIMBER FRAME PUBLICATIONS

Main characters

Theseus
Duke of Athens

Hippolyta
Queen of the Amazons

Oberon
King of the Fairies

Titania
Queen of the Fairies

Lysander

Hermia

Demetrius

Helena

The lovers

Puck
or
Robin Goodfellow
Oberon's goblin servant

Bottom
a weaver who lives in Athens

Cupid, God of Love
Often shown as a young boy, Cupid is also often shown wearing a blindfold. This is to show that love is blind – you never know where the arrows of love will hit.

Fairies
Followers of Queen Titania

Quince

Snug

Starveling

Flute

Snout

Friends of Bottom who act with him in a play

Now, fair Hippolyta, our nuptial hour
Draws on apace. Four happy days bring in
Another moon - but, O, methinks, how slow
This old moon wanes! She lingers my
 desires,
Like to a step-dame, or a dowager,
Long withering out a young man's revenue.

Our wedding day is getting near, Hippolyta.
There are still four happy days before the next
new moon - but how slowly the old one is
moving! It's hanging around like an elderly
relative who's wasting a younger man's
money, as long as she's alive.

Four days will quickly steep
 themselves in night,
Four nights will quickly dream
 away the time;
And then the moon, like to a
 silver bow
New-bent in heaven, shall
 behold the night
Of our solemnities.

Four days will
quickly pass
into night - and
we'll dream
away four
nights in no
time. Then the
new moon,
bent like a
silver bow, will
shine down on
our wedding
celebrations.

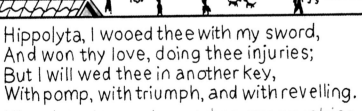

Hippolyta, I wooed thee with my sword,
And won thy love, doing thee injuries;
But I will wed thee in another key,
With pomp, with triumph, and with revelling.

Hippolyta, I wooed you when our countries
were at war, and won your love when we
were fighting one another. But our
wedding will be completely different, filled
with ceremony, splendour and fun.

1

Stand forth, Lysander...
This man hath bewitched the bosom of my child.
Thou, thou, Lysander, thou hast given her
 rhymes,
And interchanged love-tokens with my child.
Thou hast by moonlight at her window sung,
With feigning voice, verses of feigning love.

Step forward, Lysander. This man has stolen
my daughter's heart. He's given her poems
and they've exchanged lovers' presents.
He's sung at her window by moonlight -
singing in a false voice about his fake love.

With cunning hast thou filched my daughter's
 heart,
Turned her obedience, which is due to me,
To stubborn harshness. And, my gracious
 Duke,
Be it so she will not here, before your Grace,
Consent to marry with Demetrius,
I beg the ancient privilege of Athens:
As she is mine, I may dispose of her;
Which shall be either to this gentleman
Or to her death, according to our law
Immediately provided in that case.

He's cleverly stolen my daughter's heart,
turning the obedience which is due to me
into stubborn rudeness. And unless, my
lord, she agrees in your presence to marry
Demetrius, I demand that by the ancient rules
of Athens, I can do with her as I choose.
So either she marries Demetrius, or she
must be put to death, as set out in law.

What say you, Hermia? Be advised, fair maid.
To you your father should be as a god,
One that composed your beauties; yea,
 and one
To whom you are but as a form in wax
By him imprinted and within his power
To leave the figure, or disfigure it.

What do you say to that, Hermia? Take care,
girl. To you, your father should be as a god -
the one who created your beauty. You are to
him like nothing more than a soft piece of
wax, to model as he chooses - to be shaped
or squashed as he decides.

I do entreat your Grace to pardon me.
I know not by what power I am made bold,
Nor how it may concern my modesty,
In such a presence here to plead my thoughts;
But I beseech your Grace that I may know
The worst that may befall me in this case,
If I refuse to wed Demetrius.

I beg you to forgive me, please, your Grace.
I don't know what makes me able to stand up
for myself, or what people here will think of me
for doing so - but I beg your Grace to tell me
the worst that might happen to me, if I refuse
to marry Demetrius.

Either to die the death, or to abjure
Forever the society of men.
Therefore, fair Hermia, question your desires;
Know of your youth, examine well your blood,
Whether, if you yield not to your father's choice,
You can endure the livery of a nun,
For aye, to be in shady cloister mewed,
To live a barren sister all your life,
Chanting faint hymns to the cold fruitless moon.

Either you'll be put to death, or forced to lead
your life without ever seeing another man. So,
Hermia, think about what you want. Ask
yourself whether, if you refuse to marry your
father's choice, you could bear to live as a nun.
Because that's what would happen - you'd be
locked up in a convent, living an empty life,
singing weak hymns to the cold, sterile moon.

Theseus gives her until his wedding day to think about her choice.

Relent, sweet Hermia: and
  Lysander, yield
Thy crazed title to my certain right.

Give in,
sweet
Hermia.
And
Lysander,
give up
your
crazy
claim to
her. She's
mine
by right.

You have her father's love, Demetrius;
Let me have Hermia's: do you marry him.

Her father loves you, Demetrius. Why
don't you marry him, and leave Hermia
to me?

Scornful Lysander! True, he hath my love,
And what is mine my love shall render
  him;
And she is mine, and all my right of her
I do estate unto Demetrius.

Rude Lysander! It's true he has my love,
and because of that love, what's mine
shall be his. So as Hermia belongs to me,
I give her to Demetrius.

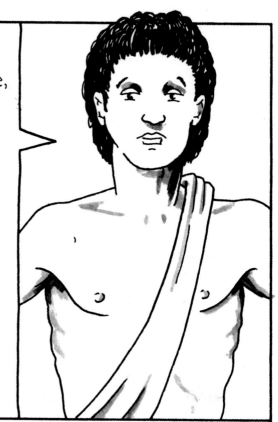

I am, my lord, as well derived as he,
As well possessed; my love is more than his...
And, which is more than all these boasts can be,
I am beloved of beauteous Hermia.
Why should not I then prosecute my right?
Demetrius, I'll avouch it to his head,
Made love to Nedar's daugther, Helena,
And won her soul; and she, sweet lady, dotes,
Devoutly dotes, dotes in idolatry,
Upon this spotted and inconstant man.

I come from as good a family as he does, my lord. I'm as good looking. I love her more than he does - and what's more important than all that, beautiful Hermia loves me. Doesn't all that give me the right to make her mine?
  Besides, Demetrius - I'll say it to his face - went after Nedar's daughter, Helena, and won her heart. And she, sweet lady, is head over heels in love with this dirty, deceiving man.

I must confess that I have heard so much,
And with Demetrius thought to have spoke thereof;
But, being overfull of self-affairs,
My mind did lose it. But, Demetrius, come;
And come, Egeus. You shall go with me;
I have some private schooling for you both.

I have to say I've heard something along those lines, and meant to have a word with Demetrius about it, but I've been so busy with my own affairs, I forgot all about it.
  But come, Demetrius and Egeus. Follow me, I've some advice I want to give you in private.

Reminding Hermia she doesn't have long to make her choice, Theseus and the others leave. Lysander and Hermia are left alone.

Ay me! For aught that I could ever read,
Could ever hear by tale or history,
The course of true love never did run
  smooth;
But either it was different in blood -

Oh dear! From all that I've ever read, or heard tell of in stories or history, true love has always met with difficulties. Either the lovers came from different backgrounds -

O cross! Too high to be enthralled to low!

Tragedy! One too rich, the other poor!

Or else misgraffed in respect of years –
Or else their ages didn't match up –

O spite! Too old to be engaged to young!
Terrible! One too old, the other too young!

Or else it stood upon the choice of friends –
Or else your choice of love was made for you by others –

O hell! To choose love by another's eyes!
Hell! To have your lover chosen for you by someone else!

Or, if there were a sympathy in choice,
War, death, or sickness did lay siege to it,
Making it momentany as a sound,
Swift as a shadow, short as any dream,
Brief as the lightning in the collied night,
That in a spleen unfolds both heaven
 and earth,
And ere a man hath power to say 'Behold!'
The jaws of darkness do devour it up:
So quick bright things come to confusion.

Or if the lovers were well matched, then
their love was attacked by war, death or
sickness; making it as quick as sound,
as hard to pin down as a shadow, as
brief as a dream or a flash of lightning
on a dark night, which, before you
can say, 'Look at that!', has gone.
Without fail, what begins brightly always
ends badly.

If then true lovers have been ever crossed,
It stands as an edict in destiny.
Then let us teach our trial patience,
Because it is a customary cross,
As due to love as thoughts and dreams and sighs,
Wishes and tears, poor fancy's followers.

If it's a fact of life that true lovers always face
such problems, there's nothing we can do. We'll
just have to learn to live with them, since these
difficulties are as much a part of love as a lover's
thoughts and dreams, sighs, wishes and tears.

There doesn't seem a way out of the problem. Then Lysander has an idea.

I have a widow aunt, a dowager
Of great revenue, and she hath no child.
From Athens is her house remote seven
 leagues,
And she respects me as her only son.
There, gentle Hermia, may I marry thee;
And to that place the sharp Athenian law
Cannot pursue us. If thou lovest me, then,
Steal forth thy father's house tomorrow night,
And in the wood, a league without the town...
There will I stay for thee.

I have a rich, old, widowed aunt.
She doesn't have any children,
and treats me like an only son.
Her house is about twenty-one
miles from Athens, far enough
away so that Athenian law can't
touch us. We can marry there.
If you love, me, then, sneak out
of your father's house tomorrow
night. I'll be waiting for you in
the wood outside town.

My good Lysander!
I swear to thee, by Cupid's strongest bow,
By his best arrow with the golden head,
By the simplicity of Venus' doves...
By all the vows that ever men have broke,
In number more than ever women spoke,
In that same place thou hast appointed me,
Tomorrow truly will I meet with thee.

Good Lysander! I promise you
by Cupid's strongest bow, by his
best arrow with its tip of gold, by
the purity of Venus' doves, by all
the promises men ever broke -
far more than women ever made
to begin with - I promise to meet
you at that agreed place.

Helena arrives.

God speed fair Helena! Whither away?

Have a safe journey, lovely Helena! Where are you off to?

Call you me fair? That 'fair' again unsay.
Demetrius loves your fair. O happy fair!...
Sickness is catching. O, were favour so,
Yours would I catch, fair Hermia, ere I go...
O, teach me how you look, and with what art
You sway the motion of Demetrius' heart.

Did you call me 'lovely'? Take that back. Demetrius loves Hermia's beauty, not mine. How lucky! People catch illnesses - why can't we catch beauty? If I could, I'd catch your looks, lovely Hermia, before I leave. Tell me the secrets of your beauty and how to win Demetrius' heart.

I frown upon him, yet he loves me still.

I frown at him, but he still loves me.

O that your frowns would teach my smiles such skill!

I wish my smiles did the same for him as your frowns.

The more I hate, the more he follows me.

The more I hate him, the more he follows me around.

The more I love, the more he hateth me.

The more I love him, the more he hates me.

His folly, Helena, is no fault of mine.

It's not my fault, Helena, that he's so stupid.

None, but your beauty: would that fault were mine!

It's all the fault of your beauty. I wish I had the same problem.

Take comfort. He no more shall see my face;
Lysander and myself will fly this place.

Well, take comfort. He won't see my face again. Lysander and I are running away together.

Telling Helena of their plans to meet in the wood, Hermia and Lysander leave.

7

How happy some o'er other some can be!
Through Athens I am thought as fair as she...
Love looks not with the eyes, but with the mind,
And therefore is winged Cupid painted blind.
Nor hath Love's mind of any judgment taste;
Wings, and no eyes, figure unheedy haste:
And therefore is Love said to be a child,
Because in choice he is so oft beguiled.
As waggish boys in game themselves forswear,
So the boy Love is perjured everywhere.
For, ere Demetrius looked on Hermia's eyne,
He hailed down oaths that he was only mine;
And when this hail some heat from Hermia felt,
So he dissolved, and showers of oaths did melt.

How much happier some people are than others - yet in Athens I'm thought as beautiful as she is. Love doesn't look with the eyes, but with the mind - which I guess is why Cupid's always pictured as being blind. Not that Love's mind can be trusted - if you fly that fast without looking where you're going, there's bound to be trouble. That's why Cupid's always pictured as a child - because he makes so many silly mistakes. In the same way as mischievous boys play tricks on each other just for fun, so Love gets cheated on everywhere.

Before Demetrius looked into Hermia's eyes, he promised he was only mine. But once he'd seen her, all his promises to me melted away.

Act 1 Scene 2

In another part of Athens, Bottom and friends have plans for a play.

Here is the scroll of every man's name, which is thought fit, through all Athens, to play in our interlude before the Duke and Duchess on his wedding day at night.

Here is a list naming every man in Athens thought fit to be in our play. It's to be performed for the Duke and Duchess, on his wedding day, at night.

First, good Peter Quince, say what the play treats on; then read the names of the actors; and so grow to a point.

First, Peter Quince, tell us what the play's about, then read the actors' names - and then stop.

Marry, our play is, 'The most lamentable comedy, and most cruel death of Pyramus and Thisbe.'

Right, our play is 'The terribly sad comedy, and cruel death of Pyramus and Thisbe.'

A very good piece of work, I assure you, and a merry. Now, good Peter Quince, call your actors by the scroll. Masters, spread yourselves.

A very good piece it is too, let me tell you - and very funny. Now, Peter Quince, call out the names of the actors you have on your list. Spread out a bit, everyone.

You, Nick Bottom, are set down for Pyramus.

You, Nick Bottom, are to play Pyramus.

A lover that kills himself, most gallant, for love.

A lover that bravely kills himself for love.

What is Pyramus? A lover, or a tyrant?

What is Pyramus? A lover, or a tough guy?

That will ask some tears in the true performing of it. If I do it, let the audience look to their eyes. I will move storms, I will condole in some measure. To the rest - yet my chief humour is for a tyrant. I could play Ercles rarely, or a part to tear a cat in, to make all split.

That part will take a bit of acting. If I play it the audience can expect to cry their eyes out. I'll make them cry floods of tears. I'll really show them grief. As for the rest though, I'd much rather play a hero. I could play Hercules incredibly well. My ranting and raving would bring the house down.

Bottom suddenly begins to sing a song that makes very little sense.

The raging rocks
And shivering shocks
Shall break the locks
 Of prison gates;
And Phibbus' car
Shall shine from far,
And make and mar
 The foolish fates.

The raging rocks
And shivering shocks
Shall break the locks
 Of prison gates;
And the sun,
 bright star
Shall shine from far
And make and mar
 The foolish fates.

This was lofty! Now name the rest of the players.

That was brilliant! Now name the other parts and their actors.

Francis Flute, the bellows mender... You must take Thisbe on you.

Francis Flute, the bellows mender - you must play the part of Thisbe.

What is Thisbe? A wandering knight?

What is Thisbe? A wandering hero?

It is the lady that Pyramus must love.

It's the woman that Pyramus loves.

Nay, faith, let not me play a woman. I have a beard coming.

Oh no! Don't make me play a woman - I'm starting to grow a beard!

That's all one. You shall play it in a mask, and you may speak as small as you will.

That doesn't matter. You can act wearing a mask and speak in a squeaky voice.

An I may hide my face, let me play Thisbe too. I'll speak in a monstrous little voice.

If I could hide my face, let me play the part of Thisbe, too. I could speak in an enormously little voice.

No, no; you must play Pyramus: and, Flute, you Thisbe... Robin Starveling, you must play Thisbe's mother... Snug, the joiner; you, the lion's part. And I hope here is a play fitted.

No, no! You must play Pyramus - and Flute, you must play Thisbe. Robin Starveling, your part is Thisbe's mother. Snug the wood-worker, you are to play the lion. There, I hope that's everything fixed up.

Have you the lion's part written? Pray you, if it be, give it me, for I am slow of study.

Have you got the lion's part written out? If you have, please give it me, because I'm a bit slow and need time to learn it.

You may do it extempore, for it is nothing but roaring.

You can make it up as you go along, because it's nothing but roaring.

Let me play the lion too. I will roar that I will do any man's heart good to hear me. I will roar, that I will make the Duke say, 'Let him roar again, let him roar again.'

Let me play the lion too! I will roar so fantastically that it would cheer anyone up to hear me. I will roar so well that the Duke will say, 'Let him roar again, let him roar again!'

An you should do it too terribly, you would fright the Duchess and the ladies, that they would shriek; and that were enough to hang us all.

If you did it too frighteningly, you would scare the Duchess and the ladies and they'd scream. And that would be enough to get us all hung.

I grant you, friends, if you should fright the ladies out of their wits, they would have no more discretion but to hang us; but I will aggravate my voice so that I will roar you as gently as any sucking dove; I will roar you an 'twere any nightingale.

I accept, friends, that if we frightened the ladies out of their wits, they'd have no choice but to hang us. But I will alter my voice so that I'll roar as sweetly as a singing bird. I will roar as if I were a nightingale

You can play no part but Pyramus... Masters, here are your parts; and I am to entreat you, request you, and desire you, to con them by tomorrow night; and meet me in the palace wood, a mile without the town, by moonlight. There will we rehearse, for if we meet in the city, we shall be dogged with company, and our devices known. In the meantime I will draw a bill of properties, such as our play wants. I pray you, fail me not.

No, you have to play Pyramus. Masters, here are your parts. And I beg you and ask and call on you to learn them by tomorrow night - and to meet me in the palace wood, a mile outside town, by moonlight. We'll rehearse there, for if we meet in the city, people will keep interrupting and find out what we're doing. In the meantime, I'll draw up a list of things we need for the play. Don't let me down.

Act 2 Scene 1

The King doth keep his revels here tonight.
Take heed the Queen come not within his sight;
For Oberon is passing fell and wrath,
Because that she as her attendant hath
A lovely boy, stolen from an Indian king;
She never had so sweet a changeling.
And jealous Oberon would have the child
Knight of his train, to trace the forests wild.
But she perforce witholds the loved boy,
Crowns him with flowers, and makes him all her
  joy.
And now they never meet in grove or green,
By fountain clear, or spangled starlight sheen,
But they do square, that all their elves for fear
Creep into acorn cups and hide them there.

The King is having a party here tonight, so make
sure the queen keeps out of his sight. Oberon
is raging mad that she has a new page boy, a
lad stolen from an Indian king. He wants to
have him as one of his own woodland followers.
  Titania, on the other hand, refuses to give up
the boy she dotes on, covers him with flowers
and makes him the centre of everything. So
now, if ever Titania and Oberon meet in the
woods, by clear waters or bright starlight, they
fight each other so fiercely, that all the
frightened elves creep into acorn cups to hide.

Either I mistake your shape and making quite,
Or else you are that shrewd and knavish sprite
Called Robin Goodfellow. Are not you he
That frights the maidens of the villagry...
And sometime make the drink to bear no barm,
Mislead night-wanderers, laughing at their harm?
Those that 'Hobgoblin' call you, and 'Sweet Puck',
You do their work, and they shall have good luck
Are not you he?

Unless I've made a big mistake about you, I'd
say you're that other-worldly mischief maker,
Robin Goodfellow. Aren't you the one that
frightens village women, kills the yeast in the
beer so it won't brew, and plays tricks on
late-night travellers, laughing at the harm they
come to because of you? Yet you bring good
luck to those that call you 'Hobgoblin' and
'Sweet Puck', Aren't you that one?

Thou speakest aright;
I am that merry wanderer of the night.
I jest to Oberon, and make him smile,
When I a fat and bean-fed horse beguile,
Neighing in likeness of a filly foal:
And sometimes lurk I in a gossip's bowl,
In very likeness of a roasted crab;
And when she drinks, against her lips I bob,
And on her withered dewlap pour the ale.
The wisest aunt, telling the saddest tale,
Sometime for three-foot stool mistaketh me;
Then slip I from her bum, down topples she,
And 'Tailor' cries, and falls into a cough;
And then the whole quire hold their hips and loffe,
And waxen in their mirth, and sneeze, and swear
A merrier hour was never wasted there.

That's me! I'm that tricky spirit of the night.
I clown about for Oberon to make him smile, like
the time I fooled a fat, yet frisky horse by
neighing as if I were a young female. Or
sometimes I hide in a gossip's mug of hot, fruity
beer, pretending to be a roasted apple. Then,
when she's drinking, I bob against her lips and
make her spill her drink all down her wrinkly neck.
   Another old woman who was telling the saddest
tale, once sat on me, thinking I was a little stool.
Then I slipped from under her backside and off
she fell, crying 'Oh my bum!' She had a fit of the
coughs, while the whole crowd held their hips and
laughed - their laughter turning to sneezes as
they claimed they've never had a funnier time.

Just then, Oberon arrives from one part of the wood, Titania from another.

Ill met by moonlight, proud Titania.
An unlucky meeting in the
moonlight, proud Titania.

Tarry, rash wanton! Am not I
thy lord?
Wait, you hot-head! Aren't
I your husband?

What, jealous Oberon! Fairies, skip hence.
I have forsworn his bed and company.
What? Oberon! Fairies, we're leaving. I won't
sleep with him, or have anything to do with him.

Then I must be thy lady. But I know
When thou hast stolen away from
  Fairyland
And in the shape of Corin sat all day,
Playing on pipes of corn, and versing love
To amorous Phillida. Why art thou here
Come from the farthest steep of India?
But that, forsooth, the bouncing Amazon,
Your buskined mistress and your warrior
  love,
To Theseus must be wedded; and you
  come
To give their bed joy and prosperity.

Then I must be your wife - but I
know of the times you've slipped
away from Fairyland and, taking
the shape of a shepherd boy, have
sat all day playing tunes while
sweet-talking some delightful girl.
  What brings you here now, all the
way from the farthest Indian hills?
It's because that gorgeous
Amazon, your leather-booted,
warrior-love is marrying Theseus
- and you've come to give them
joy and wealth.

How canst thou thus, for shame, Titania,
Glance at my credit with Hippolyta,
Knowing I know thy love to Theseus?
Didst not thou lead him through the
  glimmering night
From Perigenia, whom he ravished?
And make him with fair Aegles break his faith,
With Ariadne, and Antiopa?

How do you have the nerve to
talk about me and Hippolyta,
when I know you're in love with
Theseus? Didn't you lead him
through the night, away from
Perigenia, after he'd raped
her? And make him break with
Aegles, Ariadne and Antiopa?

These are the forgeries of jealousy:
And never since the middle summer's
  spring,
Met we on hill, in dale, forest, or mead...
To dance our ringlets to the whistling wind,
But with thy brawls thou hast disturbed our
  sport.
Therefore the winds, piping to us in vain,
As in revenge, have sucked up from the
  sea
Contagious fogs; which, falling in the land,
Hath every pelting river made so proud
That they have overborne their
  continents.

Those are nothing but the fantasies of a jealous mind. Never, since the start of midsummer, have we been able to meet on hill, in valley, forest or field to dance our circles in the whistling wind, but you've disturbed us with your noise.

And as if in revenge for all their wasted music, the winds have sucked from the sea unhealthy fogs. Falling inland, these have made every little riverlet so big, they've burst their banks.

The ox hath therefore stretched his yoke
  in vain,
The ploughman lost his sweat, and the
  green corn
Hath rotted ere his youth attained a beard.
The fold stands empty in the drowned field,
And crows are fatted with the murrion flock;
The nine-men's-morris is filled up with mud;
And the quaint mazes in the wanton green,
For lack of tread are undistinguishable.
The human mortals want their winter cheer;
No night is now with hymn or carol blest
Therefore the moon, the governess of
  floods,
Pale in her anger, washes all the air,
That rheumatic diseases do abound.
And thorough this distemperature we see
The seasons alter...

So the ox pulled his plough to no purpose, the ploughman wasted his hard work and the young corn has rotted before it can grow.

The drowned fields are empty of animals and crows have grown fat on the dying flocks. The playing fields are filled with mud and the dainty mazes have become overgrown through lack of use.

Humans feel as if it's winter, but without the things that make winter fun. No one sings hymns or carols at night. Pale with anger at all of this, the moon, controller of floods, spreads diseases through the damp air. All this disorder shows the rhythm of life has been upset.

The spring, the summer,
The childing autumn, angry winter, change
Their wonted liveries, and the mazed world,
By their increase, now knows not which is which,
And this same progeny of evils comes
From our debate, from our dissension;
We are their parents and original.

The spring and summer, fruitful autumn and harsh winter have changed their nature. A world turned upside down by such changes doesn't know what's going on. And all these evils come about because of our argument, our quarrel. We caused these problems.

Do you amend it, then; it lies in you.
Why should Titania cross her
   Oberon?
I do but beg a little changeling boy,
To be my henchman.

Put things right, then. You have the power. Why should Titania want to fight with her Oberon? All I'm asking is to have the stolen boy as my follower.

Set your heart at rest.
The fairy land buys not the child of me.
His mother was a vot'ress of my order...
And for her sake do I rear up her boy,
And for her sake I will not part with him.

Be certain of one thing. The whole of fairyland couldn't buy the child from me. His mother worshipped me, and for her sake I'm bringing up her boy - and for her sake I'll not part with him.

Titania and her fairies leave.

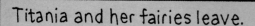

Well, go thy way. Thou shalt not from this grove
Till I torment thee for this injury.
My gentle Puck, come hither. Thou rememberest
Since once I sat upon a promontory
And heard a mermaid on a dolphin's back,
Uttering such dulcet and harmonious breath,
That the rude sea grew civil at her song,
And certain stars shot madly from their spheres
To hear the sea maid's music?

Alright, go then. But you're not leaving this wood till I've punished you for your wrong to me.
   Come over here, Puck. You remember that time I was sitting on a rocky coast when I heard a mermaid? She was riding on a dolphin's back. Her singing was so sweet and pure that the rough sea grew calm and stars shot madly about the sky on hearing the sea-girl's song.

That very time I saw (but thou couldst not)
Flying between the cold moon and the earth,
Cupid all armed; a certain aim he took
At a fair vestal throned by the west,
And loosed his love-shaft smartly from his bow
As it should pierce a hundred thousand hearts;
But I might see young Cupid's fiery shaft
Quenched in the chaste beams of the watery
 moon;
And the imperial vot'ress passed on,
In maiden meditation, fancy-free.

Just then I saw (although you couldn't) the boy
Cupid flying between the cold moon and earth.
He had his bow and arrows with him, and took
aim at a lovely young queen of the western
world. His love-arrow flew so fast from his bow,
as if to pass through a hundred thousand
hearts. Yet I could see young Cupid's blazing
arrow put out by the watery moon's cold light.
So the pure young royal passed on, her
thoughts free from the power of love.

Yet marked I where the bolt of Cupid fell:
It fell upon a little western flower...
Fetch me that flower; the herb I showed thee
 once:
The juice of it on sleeping eyelids laid
Will make or man or woman madly dote
Upon the next live creature that it sees.
Fetch me this herb.

I saw where the arrow fell. It landed on a little
flower growing in the west. Juice from it, when
put on a sleeper's eyelids, will make that man
or woman fall madly in love with the next living
creature seen on waking. Bring me this plant.

I'll put a girdle round about
 the earth
In forty minutes.

I'll fly round the world in forty
minutes.

Having once this juice,
I'll watch Titania when she is asleep,
And drop the liquor of it in her eyes:
The next thing then she, waking, looks upon...
She shall pursue it with the soul of love.
And ere I take this charm from off her sight,
(As I can take it with another herb)
I'll make her render up her page to me.

Once I have this juice I'll watch Titania when
she's asleep, and drop the liquid in her eyes.
Then she'll fall totally in love with the next thing
she sees on waking. And before removing the
spell from her eyes (which I can with another
plant), I'll make her give me her servant boy.

I love thee not, therefore pursue me not...
Do I entice you? Do I speak you fair?
Or, rather, do I not in plainest truth
Tell you, I do not nor I cannot love you.

I don't love you, so stop following me. Am I leading you on? Have I been flirting with you? In fact, haven't I been trying to tell you in the plainest way, that I don't and can't, love you?

And even for that do I love you the more.
I am your spaniel; and, Demetrius,
The more you beat me, I will fawn on you.
Use me but as your spaniel; spurn me, strike me,
Neglect me, lose me; only give me leave,
Unworthy as I am, to follow you.

And even for that I love you more. I'm your dog, and the more you beat me, Demetrius, the more I'll be your slave. Treat me no better than your dog, reject me, hit me, ignore me, lose me - only let me follow you, worthless as I am.

Tempt not too much the hatred of my spirit;
For I am sick when I do look on thee.

Don't push me too far. It makes me feel sick to look at you.

You do impeach your modesty too much,
To leave the city and commit yourself
Into the hands of one that loves you not;
To trust the opportunity of night,
And the ill counsel of a desert place,
With the rich worth of your virginity.

You've put your reputation at real risk by leaving the city and putting yourself in the hands of someone that hates you. Given the darkness and danger of this lonely place, aren't you afraid you'll be raped?

And I am sick when I look not on you.

And I feel sick when I'm not looking at you.

Your virtue is my privilege: for that
It is not night when I do see your face,
Therefore I think I am not in the night;
Nor doth this wood lack worlds of company,
For you, in my respect, are all the world.
Then how can it be said I am alone,
When all the world is here to look on me?

Your good nature guarantees my safety.
Besides, it's never dark when I see your
face, so I can't believe it's really night. Nor
does this wood lack
crowds of people -
for as far as I'm
concerned, you're
my whole world.
So how could it be
said I'm alone, if
the whole world is
here looking at me?

I will not stay thy questions.
 Let me go!
Or, if thou follow me, do not
 believe
But I shall do thee mischief
 in the wood.
I'm not
putting
up with
any more
of your
questions.
Let me go!
If you
follow me,
don't think
I won't do
you some
harm in
the wood.

Demetrius
leaves. Not
put off by his
threats, Helena
follows him.
 Feeling sorry
for her, Oberon
decides to help
her with the
magic flower of
love, which
Puck was able
to find.

Hast thou the flower there? Do you have the flower there?

Ay, there it is. Yes, it's here.

I pray thee, give it me.
I know a bank where the wild thyme blows,
Where oxlips and the nodding violet grows,
Quite overcanopied with luscious woodbine,
With sweet musk-roses, and with eglantine.
There sleeps Titania sometime of the night,
Lulled in these flowers with dances and delight...
And with the juice of this I'll streak her eyes,
And make her full of hateful fantasies.

Give it to me, please. I know a flowery bank where
wild thyme, oxslips and violets grow, roofed
over with honeysuckle and sweet-smelling roses.
 Titania sleeps part of the night there, soothed
asleep among the flowers after dancing and
other delights. I'll dab her eyelids with this juice,
and that way fill her mind with hateful thoughts.

Take thou some of it, and seek through
  this grove:
A sweet Athenian lady is in love
With a disdainful youth. Anoint his eyes;
But do it when the next thing he espies
May be the lady. Thou shalt know the man
By the Athenian garments he hath on.
Effect it with some care that he may prove
More fond on her than she upon her love.

Take some of this and search through
the wood for a rude young man with
whom a sweet Athenian lady is in love.
  Paint his eyes with the juice, but do it
when the next thing he sees will be the
lady. You'll know the man by the Athenian
clothes he's wearing. Take great care
that he falls more in love with her than
she with him.

Act 2 Scene 2

Titania is with her fairy followers.

Come, now a roundel and a fairy song;
Then, for the third part of a minute, hence –
Some to kill cankers in the musk-rose buds,
Some war with reremice for their leathern
  wings
To make my small elves coats, and some
  keep back
The clamorous owl that nightly hoots and
  wonders
At our quaint spirits. Sing me now asleep;
Then to your offices, and let me rest.

Let's have a dance and
a fairy song. Then, after
a few seconds, fly away
– some to kill caterpillars
in the rose buds; some
to fight bats for their
leather wings, from
which we'll make coats
for the smallest elves;
and some to silence
the noisy owl that nightly
hoots surprise at our
dainty ways.
  First, sing to me, then
get off to your work and
let me rest.

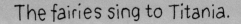

The fairies sing to Titania.

You spotted snakes with double tongue,
  Thorny hedgehogs, be not seen;
Newts and blindworms, do no wrong,
  Come not near our Fairy Queen.

You spotted snakes with long forked tongues,
  Thorn-covered hedgehogs, don't be seen;
Newts and slow-worms, do no harm,
  Keep well clear of our Fairy Queen.

Weaving spiders, come not here;
  Hence you long-legged spinners, hence!
Beetles black, approach not near;
  Worm nor snail, do no offence.

Web-weaving spiders, don't come here;
  Clear off, long-legged spiders, go!
Black-shelled beetles, don't come near;
  Worms and snails, don't trouble us, no.

The fairies leave as Titania sleeps - and Oberon arrives with the magic juice.

What thou seest when thou dost wake,
Do it for thy true-love take;
Love and languish for his sake.
Be it ounce, or cat, or bear,
Pard, or boar with bristled hair,
In thy eye that shall appear
When thou wak'st, it is thy dear.
Wake when some vile thing is near!

Fall in love with whatever you see on first waking up. Suffer all love's miseries for his sake - whether it's a lynx, cat or bear, leopard or boar with bristled hair. What you see when you wake is what you'll love. Make sure what's near is something truly horrible.

Lysander and Hermia arrive.

Fair love, you faint with wandering in the
  wood;
And to speak troth, I have forgot our way.
We'll rest us, Hermia, if you think it good,
And tarry for the comfort of the day.

My love, you're tired out with all this wandering round the wood. And to tell you the truth, I've forgotten the way. If you agree, I think we should rest until tomorrow when things will be better.

Be it so, Lysander.
  Find you out a bed.
For I upon this bank
  will rest my head.
I agree, Lysander.
Find yourself a bed.
I'll settle down on
this bank.

As they are not yet married, Hermia insists they sleep apart. Puck arrives. He thinks the two can't be lovers because they're lying so far from one another - and because of this decides Hermia must be Helena and that Lysander is Demetrius.

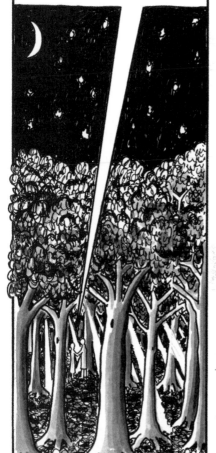

Through the forest have I gone,
But Athenian found I none...
Night and silence - Who is here?
Weeds of Athens he doth wear:
This is he my master said
Despised the Athenian maid...
Churl, upon thy eyes I throw
All the power this charm doth owe.
When thou wak'st, let love forbid
Sleep his seat on thy eyelid.
So, awake when I am gone;
For I must now to Oberon.
I've been all through the wood and found no-one from Athens. It's dark and quiet. Who's here? He's wearing Athenian clothes - this is the one my master said rejected the Athenian maid.
  You scum, upon your eyes I place all the power this magic juice contains. When you wake, let love's pains stop you from ever sleeping again. Wake up when I've gone - I have to go and find Oberon.

As Puck leaves, Demetrius arrives, followed by Helena. He tells her to leave him alone and sets off further into the wood without her.
  Helena sees Lysander, and wakes him up. Being the first thing he sees on opening his eyes, he falls instantly in love with her.

Lysander, if you live, good sir, awake.
Lysander! If you're alive, wake up!

And run through fire I will for thy sweet
  sake!
Transparent Helena! Nature shows art,
That through thy bosom makes me see
  thy heart.
Where is Demetrius? O, how fit a word
Is that vile name to perish on my sword!
I'd run through fire for you! Clear-skinned Helena! By a gift of nature I can see through your breast to your heart. Where's Demetrius? How right it is that one with that foul name should die on my sword!

Helena thinks Lysander's making fun of her.

Wherefore was I to this keen mockery born?
When at your hands did I deserve this scorn?...
But fare you well: perforce I must confess
I thought you lord of more true gentleness.
O, that a lady, of one man refused,
Should of another therefore be abused!

Why was I born to be made fun of like this?
What have I done to you to deserve this
unkindness? Goodbye. I have to say I
thought you a person with better manners.
It's not fair that a woman rejected by one
man should as a result be abused by another!

Helena leaves.

She sees not Hermia. Hermia, sleep thou there,
And never mayst thou come Lysander near!
For, as a surfeit of the sweetest things
The deepest loathing to the stomach brings,
Or as the heresies that men do leave
Are hated most of those they did decieve,
So thou, my surfeit and my heresy,
Of all be hated, but the most by me!

She hasn't seen Hermia. Carry on sleeping,
Hermia, and never come near me again. For
just as it's the sweet things you eat too much
of that you end hating the most; or the lies which
are found out that are most hated by the people
taken in by them - so you to me are like that
over-eaten sweet thing and a lie. May you be
hated by everyone, but most of all by me!

Lysander leaves to follow Helena. Hermia
wakes - and finds herself alone.

Lysander! What, removed? Lysander! Lord!
What, out of hearing? Gone? No sound, no
  word?
Alack, where are you? Speak, and if you hear;
Speak, of all loves! I swoon almost with fear.
No? Then I well perceive you are not nigh.
Either death or you I'll find immediately.

Lysander! What, gone away? Lysander! Lord!
What, too far off to hear? Gone? Not a sound
or word? Where are you? Speak. If you hear
me, speak, for goodness' sake!
 I'm almost fainting with fear. No? Then
I guess you can't be near. Either I'll find
you, or my death at once.

Act 3 Scene 1

Bottom and friends have arrived in the wood. They haven't seen Titania sleeping nearby.

Here's a marvail's convenient place for our rehearsal. This green plot shall be our stage, this hawthorn brake our tiring-house, and we will do it in action as we will do it before the Duke.

Here's a very convenient place for us to practice. This green spot shall be our stage, behind that hawthorn bush shall be our dressing room. We'll act everything out exactly as we'll perform it for the Duke.

There are things in this comedy of Pyramus and Thisbe that will never please. First, Pyramus must draw a sword to kill himself, which the ladies cannot abide. How answer you that?

There are things in this comedy about Pyramus and Thisbe that people will never find funny. First, Pyramus has to draw a sword and kill himself - which the ladies will hate. What do you say to that?

By'r lakin, a parlous fear.

Oh no! That's a real danger.

I believe we must leave the killing out, when all is done.

I guess we'll have to leave the killing out, in that case.

Not a whit. I have a device to make all well. Write me a prologue, and let the prologue seem to say, we will do no harm with our swords, and that Pyramus is not killed indeed; and, for the more better assurance, tell them that I, Pyramus, am not Pyramus, but Bottom the weaver. This will put them out of fear.

Not a bit of it. I have a plan to make it alright. Write me an introduction, and let it suggest that we won't be hurting anyone with our swords and that Pyramus isn't really killed. Even better, tell them that I'm not really Pyramus at all, but Bottom the weaver. That will stop them worrying.

Will not the ladies be afeard of the lion?

Won't the ladies be afraid of the lion?

I fear it, I promise you.

I'm afraid so - I'm sure they will be.

Masters, you ought to consider with yourselves. To bring in - God shield us! - a lion among ladies, is a most dreadful thing. For there is not a more fearful wild-fowl than your lion living; and we ought to look to't.

You need to think about this, friends. To bring on a lion amongst ladies is a terrible thing to do, for heaven's sake. There's not any wild bird now living more terrible than a lion - so we need to sort that out.

Therefore another prologue must tell he is not a lion.

Well then, we must have another introduction to say he's not a lion.

Puck arrives.

What hempen homespuns have we swaggering here,
So near the cradle of the Fairy Queen?
What, a play toward? I'll be an auditor;
An actor, too perhaps, if I see cause.

Who are these clowns causing all this noise so near the Fairy Queen?
What! A play's about to start? I'll be in the audience - and maybe take part too, if I get the chance.

25

The actors begin to rehearse.

Thisbe, the flowers of odious savours sweet—

Thisbe, the flowers have odious sweet smells...

Odours, odours. *Odorous, odorous.*

– odours savours sweet.
So hath thy breath, my dearest Thisbe dear.
But hark, a voice! Stay thou but here awhile,
And by and by I will to thee appear.

...odorous sweet smells – just like your breath, my dearest Thisbe. But wait, I hear a voice. Stay here. I'll be back in a moment.

A stranger Pyramus than e'er played here!
He'll come back much stranger than he left!

Bottom leaves the stage and goes behind the thorn bush. Puck follows him there and gives him the head of an ass (or donkey).

Must I speak now?
Do I have to speak now?

Ay, marry, must you; for you must understand he goes but to see a noise that he heard, and is to come again.
Yes, you must. You have to understand that he's only gone to see a noise he heard, and will be back later.

Bottom appears from behind the bush.

If I were fair, Thisbe, I were only thine.
If I were good-looking, Thisbe, I'd be only yours.

O monstrous! O strange! We are haunted. Pray, masters, fly, masters! Help!... Bless thee, Bottom! Bless thee! Thou art translated.
How horrible! How terrifying! We're haunted! Run away, friends! Help! God save you, Bottom, God save you – you've been turned into a monster!

I see their knavery. This is to make an ass of me; to fright me, if they could. But I will not stir from this place, do what they can. I will walk up and down here, and will sing, that they shall hear I am not afraid.

I see their game. This is to make me look a fool - to frighten me, if they could. But I'm not moving. I'll walk up and down here and sing, so they'll know I'm not afraid.

Bottom sings.

What angel wakes me from my flowery bed?...
I pray thee, gentle mortal, sing again:
Mine ear is much enamoured of thy note;
So is mine eye enthralled to thy shape;
And thy fair virtue's force perforce doth move me
On the first view to say, to swear, I love thee.

What angel wakes me from my bed of flowers? I beg you, sweet human, sing again. My ears love your singing; my eyes love your looks - and your strong yet gentle personality forces me to say, on first sight, I love you.

Methinks, mistress, you should have little reason for that. And yet, to say the truth, reason and love keep little company together nowadays; the more the pity that some honest neighbours will not make them friends.

I'm sure, madam, that you've little reason for saying that. And yet, to speak the truth, reason and love don't seem to have much to do with one another these days - it's a shame that an honest friend can't bring them back together.

Thou art as wise as thou art beautiful.
You are as clever as you are beautiful.

Not so, neither; but if I had wit enough to get out of this wood, I have enough to serve mine own turn.

Not really. But if I had enough brain to get out of this wood, I'd have as much as I need.

Out of this wood do not desire to go;
Thou shalt remain here, whether thou wilt or no.
I am a spirit of no common rate;
The summer still doth tend upon my state,
And I do love thee. Therefore, go with me.
I'll give thee fairies to attend on thee,
And they shall fetch thee jewels from the deep,
And sing, while thou on pressed flowers dost sleep;
And I will purge thy mortal grossness so,
That thou shall like an airy spirit go.
Peaseblossom! Cobweb! Moth and Mustardseed!

Don't ever think of leaving this wood. You're going
to stay here whether you want to or not. I'm no
ordinary spirit - even the summer itself is at my
command - and I love you. So stay with me.

I'll give you fairy servants who'll fetch you jewels
from the bottom of the sea and who'll sing to you
as you sleep on a bed of pressed flowers. I'll free
you from being human so that you may fly in the air
like a fairy.

Peaseblossom! Cobweb! Moth! Mustardseed!

Four fairies arrive.

Be kind and courteous to this gentleman;
Hop in his walks, and gambol in his eyes;
Feed him with apricocks and dewberries,
With purple grapes, green figs, and mulberries...
And pluck the wings from painted butterflies,
To fan the moonbeams from his sleeping eyes.
Nod to him, elves, and do him courtesies...
Come, wait upon him. Lead him to my bower.

Be kind and
polite to this
gentleman.
Dance ahead as
he walks, skipping
about before his eyes.
Feed him with apricots
and blackberries,
purple grapes, green
figs and mulberries.
Pluck the wings
from bright butterflies
to fan moonbeams
from his sleeping
eyes. Bow to him,
elves, and show
him all respect. Look
after him. Lead him
to my resting place.

Act 3 Scene 2

Oberon is waiting for Puck, who arrives from another part of the wood.

I wonder if Titania be awaked:
Then, what it was that next came in her eye,
Which she must dote on, in extremity.
Here comes my messenger. How now, mad
  spirit!
What night-rule now about this haunted grove?

I wonder if Titania has woken up yet. If so,
I wonder what it was she first saw that she's
fallen madly in love with.
  Here's my messenger. Hi, mad spirit! What's
going on in this haunted wood tonight?

My mistress with a monster is in love.

My mistress has fallen in love with a
monster!

This falls out better than I could devise.
But hast thou yet latched the Athenian's eyes
With the love juice, as I did bid thee do?

This is even
better than I
could have
planned. But
have you
dabbed the
Athenian's
eyes with
love juice,
as I ordered
you?

I took him sleeping - that is
  finished too -
And the Athenian woman by
  his side;
That, when he waked, of
  force she must be eyed.

I did it as he slept -
and in such a way
that when he woke
the first thing he
would have to see
would be the
Athenian woman
nearby him.

Looking for Lysander,
Hermia meets up with
Demetrius. She is
sure he must have
murdered her lover.

Stand close: this is
  the same Athenian.

Keep out of sight. This
is the Athenian.

This is the woman,
  but not this the man.

This is the woman, but
it's not the same man.

O, why rebuke you him that loves you so?
Lay breath so bitter on your bitter foe.

Why are you so hard on someone who loves you so much? Save your cruellest words for your worst enemies.

Out, dog! Out, cur! Thou driv'st me past the bounds
Of maiden's patience. Hast thou slain him, then?
Henceforth be never numbered among men!

Get out of my sight, you dog! You've pushed me way beyond what any girl could stand. Have you killed him, then? From now on you're not fit to be called a human being.

You spend your passion on a misprised mood:
I am not guilty of Lysander's blood;
Nor is he dead, for aught that I can tell.

You've got yourself worked up about nothing. I didn't kill Lysander. He isn't even dead, as far as I know.

I pray thee, tell me then that he is well.
Tell me then that he's safe.

An if I could, what should I get therefore?
And if I did, what would I gain by it?

A privilege, never to see me more;
And from thy hated presence part I so.
See me no more, whether he be dead or no.

The reward of never seeing me again. I'm leaving your hated company right now. Don't try to see me whether he's dead or not.

Hermia leaves.

There is no following her in this fierce vein.
Here therefore for a while I will remain.

There's no point in following her when she's in such a bad mood - so I'll stay here for a while.

Demetrius falls asleep.

What hast thou done? Thou hast mistaken quite,
And laid the love juice on some true-love's sight.
Of thy misprision must perforce ensue
Some true love turned, and not a false turned true.

What have you done? You've got it all wrong, and
placed the love juice on a true lover's eyes.
What's certain to happen now, because of your
mistake, is that one who truely loved will be turned
from his love - not a false lover made a true one.

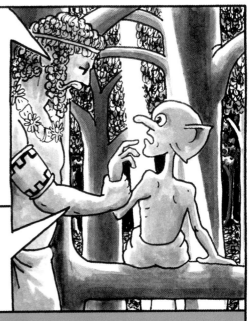

Then fate o'errules, that, one man holding troth,
A million fail, confounding oath on oath.

That's life. For every man who keeps his word, a
million fail - breaking one promise after another.

Oberon sends Puck to find Helena while he paints the magic juice on Demetrius' sleeping eyes.

Flower of this purple dye,
Hit with Cupid's archery.
Sink in apple of his eye.
When his love he doth
 espy,
Let her shine as gloriously
As the Venus of the sky.
When thou wak'st, if she
 be by,
Beg of her for remedy.

Let this purple juice, from
the flower hit by Cupid's
arrow, sink into his eye.
   When he next sees his
love, let her shine out as
brilliantly as Venus in the
night sky.
   When you wake, if she's
near, beg her to take
you back.

Puck returns.

Captain of our fairy band,
Helena is here at hand;
And the youth, mistook by me,
Pleading for a lover's fee.
Shall we their fond pageant see?
Lord, what fools these mortals be!

Oberon, king of our fairy band,
Helena is near - as well as the
young man I made a mistake
about. He's begging for her love.
Shall we watch what happens?
Humans are so ridiculous!

Stand aside. The
 noise they make
Will cause
 Demetrius to
 awake.

Stand back.
Their noise
will wake up
Demetrius.

Then will two at once woo one -
That must needs be sport alone:
And those things do best
 please me
That befall prepost'rously.

Then both men will be trying to
win her. That will be so funny.
   I'm always amused by the
   silly things that go on.

Lysander and Helena arrive.

Why should you think that I should woo in scorn?
  Scorn and derision never come in tears.
Look, when I vow, I weep; and vows so born,
  In their nativity all truth appears.
How can these things in me seem scorn to you,
Bearing the badge of faith, to prove them true?

What makes you think I'm pretending to love you for a joke? You never see tears with that sort of cruel fun. Look, I'm crying as I promise to be true. Promises mixed with tears have to be for real. How can you treat what I say as a nasty joke, when my tears prove my love to be true?

You do advance your cunning more and more.
  When truth kills truth, O devilish-holy fray!
These vows are Hermia's. Will you give her o'er?
  Weigh oath with oath, and you will nothing weigh;
Your vows to her and me, put in two scales,
Will even weigh, and both as light as tales.

You're trying very hard to persuade me. What a terrible thing, when one truth destroys another! Your promises belong to Hermia - are you giving her up? Weigh one promise against another, and you'll have nothing. Your promises to her and me will cancel each other out, all just empty words.

I had no judgment when
  to her I swore.

I wasn't thinking straight when I promised those things to her.

Nor none, in my mind,
  now you give her o'er.

You're not now you're giving her up, as far as I can tell.

Demetrius wakes up, sees Helena - and falls madly back in love with her.

O Helen, goddess, nymph, perfect, divine!
To what, my love, shall I compare thine eyne?
Crystal is muddy. O, how ripe in show
Thy lips, those kissing cherries, tempting grow!
That pure congeled white, high Taurus' snow,
Fanned with the easter wind, turns to a crow
When thou hold'st up thy hand: O, let me kiss
This princess of pure white, this seal of bliss!

Beautiful Helena, you goddess! You're perfect! To what should I compare your eyes, my love? They make crystals look muddy. Your lips are like two ripe cherries, kissing each other as they meet - and tempting me to kiss them! When you hold up your hand, white, packed, wind-blown mountain snow looks black. My fair princess, let me kiss you and go straight to paradise!

O spite! O hell! I see you all are bent
To set against me for your merriment:
If you were civil, and knew courtesy,
You would not do me thus much injury.
Can you not hate me, as I know you do,
But you must join in souls to mock me too?

Such spite and cruelty! I can see you're
both determined to make fun of me! If either
of you were gentlemen or had any manners,
you wouldn't treat me this way. Even hating
me as much as I know you do, do you have
to join together to make fun of me like this?

You are unkind, Demetrius. Be not so,
For you love Hermia - this you know I know -
And here, with all good will, with all my heart,
In Hermia's love I yield you up my part;
And yours of Helena to me bequeath,
Whom I do love, and will do till my death.

You're being unkind, Demetrius. Don't be
like that. You know I know you're in love
with Hermia - so with all good will, with all
my heart, I give her up to you. In return,
you release Helena to me. I love her,
and will for as long as I live.

Lysander, keep thy Hermia; I will none.
If e'er I loved her, all that love is gone.

Keep your Hermia, Lysander. I don't want
her. If I ever loved her, that love is dead.

Hermia arrives. She wants to know why Lysander left her alone in the wood.

What love could press
    Lysander from my side?

What love could have
forced Lysander to
leave me?

Lysander's love, that would not let him
    bide,
Fair Helena - who more engilds the night
Than all yon fiery oes and eyes of light.
Why seek'st thou me? Could not this
    make thee know,
The hate I bare thee made me leave
    thee so?

It was the love of my life,
Helena, who wouldn't let me
stay. She lights up the night
more brightly than all those
fiery stars up there.
    Why have you come
looking for me? Don't you
realise that I left you
because I hate you?

You speak not as you
think: it cannot be.

You can't mean that.
It can't be true.

Lo, she is one of the confederacy!
Now I perceive they have conjoined all three
To fashion this false sport in spite of me.
Injurious Hermia! Most ungrateful maid!
Have you conspired, have you with these contrived
To bait me with this foul derision?

So, she's in on it too! Now I see that all three of
them have joined together to play this horrid joke,
to get at me. Vicious Hermia! Spiteful girl! Have
you plotted and planned with the others to hurt
me with this cruel humour?

Is all the counsel that we two have shared,
The sisters' vows, the hours that we have spent,
When we have chid the hasty-footed time
For parting us - O, is all forgot?
All schooldays' friendship, childhood innocence?
We, Hermia, like two artificial gods,
Have with our needles created both one flower,
Both on one sampler, sitting on one cushion,
Both warbling of one song, both in one key;
As if our hands, our sides, voices, and minds,
Had been incorporate...

Have you forgotten all our talks, our sisterly
promises; the hours we've spent together, cursing
the time as it rushed us towards that moment we
had to part? Have you forgotten all the days of
our friendship, as small children and schoolgirls?
Like two lords of creation, we've worked with our
needles, sewing the same flower on the same
piece of cloth, sharing one cushion, both singing
the same song in perfect harmony - as if our
hands, our sides, voices and minds had been one.

And you will rent our ancient love asunder.
To join with men in scorning your poor friend?
It is not friendly, 'tis not maidenly.
Our sex, as well as I, may chide you for it,
Though I alone do feel the injury.

And you're willing to tear our old love apart by
joining these men in their joke on your poor friend?
It's not kind - it's no way for a female to behave. And
it's not only me - any woman would criticize what
you're doing, even though I alone feel the pain of it.

I am amazed at your passionate words.
I scorn you not...
I understand not what you mean by this.

I'm amazed at your hot words. I'm not making fun
of you. I don't know what you're talking about.

Ay, do! Persever, counterfeit sad looks,
Make mouths upon me when I turn my back;
Wink each at other; hold the sweet jest up...
But fare ye well. 'Tis partly my own fault,
Which death or absence soon shall remedy.

That's it! Keep pretending to look sad, then pull faces at me when I turn my back. Wink at each other - keep the joke going. Goodbye. I know it's partly my own fault, but my death or disappearance will soon sort things out.

Stay, gentle Helena; hear my excuse:
My love, my life, my soul, fair Helena!...
Helen, I love thee; by my life, I do!
I swear by that which I will lose for thee,
To prove him false that says I love thee not.

Wait, Helena. Listen to me - my love, my life, my soul, beautiful Helena! I love you, on my life I do! I promise I'm willing to lose my life fighting anyone who says I don't love you.

Do you not jest?...
Am not I Hermia? Are not you
  Lysander?
I am as fair now as I was erstwhile.
Since night you loved me; yet
  since night you left me.
Why, then you left me - O, the gods
  forbid -
In earnest, shall I say?

Are you joking? Aren't I Hermia? Aren't you Lysander? Am I not as good-looking now as I was before? Earlier tonight you were in love with me, yet earlier tonight you left me. So, when you left me - God help me - you really meant it.

Ay, by my life!
And never did desire to see thee more.
Therefore be out of hope, of question,
  of doubt;
Be certain, nothing truer - 'tis no jest
That I do hate thee, and love Helena.

You've got it! When I left, I never wanted to see you again. So give up any bit of hope. Don't be in any doubt - nothing could be more true: I'm not joking when I say that I hate you and love Helena.

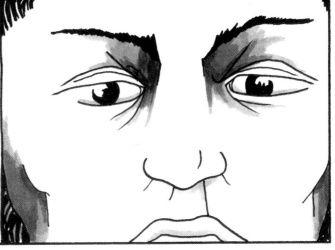

O me! You juggler! You canker-blossom!
You thief of love! What, have you come by night
And stol'n my love's heart from him?

You cheat! You worm! You thief of love! What, have you sneaked up in the dark and stolen my lover's heart?

Fine, i'faith!
Have you no modesty, no maiden shame,
No touch of bashfulness? What, will you tear
Impatient answers from my gentle tongue?
Fie, fie! You counterfeit, you puppet, you!

What? Have you no shame? Don't you have any thought for others? Are you determined to force harsh words from my gentle tongue? Ha! You cheat, you midget!

'Puppet'? Why so? – Ay, that way goes the game.
Now I perceive that she hath made compare
Between our statures; she hath urged her height,
And with her personage, her tall personage,
Her height, forsooth, she hath prevailed with him.
And are you grown so high in his esteem,
Because I am so dwarfish and so low?
How low am I, thou painted maypole? Speak!
How low am I? I am not yet so low
But that my nails can reach unto thine eyes.

Midget? What? I see what you're getting at. Now I understand that she's been comparing our height. She's made a thing about how much taller she is, her tall stature. She's used her extra height to win him over. And you've risen so high in his opinion because I am so stunted and low. How low am I, you painted stick? Answer me! How low am I? I am not quite so low that my nails can't scratch your eyes out.

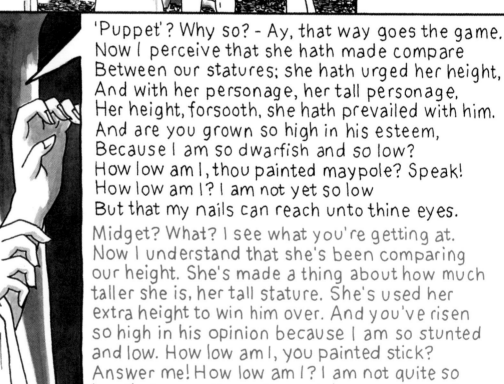

I pray you, though you mock me, gentlemen...
Let her not strike me. You perhaps may think,
Because she is something lower than myself,
That I can match her.

Even though you're making fun of me, gentlemen, I beg you not to let her hit me. Maybe you think that because she's a good bit shorter than me, I could match her in a fight.

'Lower'? Hark, again!

Listen to that - 'shorter', again!

O, when she is angry, she is keen and shrewd!
She was a vixen when she went to school,
And though she be but little, she is fierce.

She has a sharp, vicious tongue when she's angry. She was like a wild animal when she was at school - and though she's only little, she's fierce.

'Little' again! Nothing but 'low' and 'little'!
Why will you suffer her to flout me thus?
Let me come to her.

'Little' again! Nothing but 'short' and 'little'! Why do you let her insult me like this? Let me get at her!

Get you gone, you dwarf;
You minimus of hindering knot-grass made:
You bead, you acorn!

Clear off, you dwarf; you stunted straw-doll! You bead, you acorn!

You are too officious
In her behalf that scorns your services.
Let her alone. Speak not of Helena,
Take not her part; for, if thou dost intend
Never so little show of love to her,
Thou shalt aby it.

You're way out of line there! Helena doesn't want your help. Leave Hermia alone. Don't speak about Helena or take her side - for if you try to show even a hint of love for her, I'll make you suffer.

Now follow, if thou dar'st, to try whose right,
Of thine or mine, is most in Helena.

In that case, follow me - if you have the guts - to somewhere we can fight out which of us has the most right to Helena's love.

Follow! Nay, I'll go with thee, cheek by jowl.

Follow you? Never! I'm not following behind you - we'll go together side by side.

Lysander and Demetrius leave.

You, mistress, all this coil is 'long of you:
Nay, go not back.

All this upset was caused by you, woman! There's no need to step back in fear.

I will not trust you, I,
Nor longer stay in your curst company.
Your hands than mine are quicker for a fray,
My legs are longer, though, to run away.

I don't trust you and I'm not staying in your hated company. Your hands are quicker than mine for a fight - but my long legs are better for running away!

Helena runs off and Hermia chases after her.

This is thy negligence. Still thou mistak'st,
Or else committ'st thy knaveries wilfully.

This is all your fault. Either it was a mistake, or else you did it on purpose.

Believe me, King of Shadows, I mistook.
Did not you tell me I should know the man
By the Athenian garments he had on?
And so far blameless proves my enterprise,
That I have 'nointed an Athenian's eyes;
And so far am I glad it so did sort,
As this their jangling I esteem a sport.

Believe me, King of the Night, it was a mistake. Didn't you tell me I would know the man by his Athenian clothes? So you surely can't blame me for dabbing the juice on an Athenian's eyes.
Anyway, I'm glad it turned out the way it has, since I find all this arguing very funny.

Thou see'st these lovers seek a place to fight:
Hie, therefore, Robin, overcast the night;
The starry welkin cover thou anon
With drooping fog as black as Acheron,
And lead these testy rivals so astray,
As one come not within another's way.
Like to Lysander sometime frame thy tongue,
Then stir Demetrius up with bitter wrong;
And sometime rail thou like Demetrius.
And from each other look thou lead them thus.
Till o'er their brows death-counterfeiting sleep
With leaden legs and batty wings doth creep.

You can see these lovers are looking for a place to fight. Hurry, therefore Robin, and cover the sky in a fog as black as the River of Doom. Then lead these angry rivals all over the place, so they can't find one another.
Sometimes call out as if you were Lysander to stir up Demetrius' anger. Then sometimes shout out as if you were Demetrius. In this way drive them apart, till a death-like sleep creeps up on them with heavy legs and silent wings.

Then crush this herb into Lysander's eye,
Whose liquor hath this virtuous property,
To take from thence all error with his might,
And make his eyeballs roll with wonted sight.
When next they wake, all this derision
Shall seem a dream and fruitless vision,
And back to Athens shall the lovers wend,
With league whose date till death shall never end.
Whiles I in this affair do thee employ,
I'll to my queen and beg her Indian boy;
And then I will her charmed eye release
From monster's view, and all things shall be peace.

When you've done that, squeeze this herb over Lysander's eyes. Its juice will cure all his problems and make his eyes see as they used to. When he wakes, all this confusion will seem like nothing but a dream. The lovers will return to Athens and live happily for the rest of their lives. While you're about this business of mine, I'll go to Titania to ask her for the Indian boy. Then I'll lift the spell from her eyes, she won't love the monster any more, and everything will be fine.

As ordered by Oberon, Puck leads Lysander and Demetrius around the wood. First he calls to Lysander pretending to be Demetrius - then the other way round! All four lovers have been surrounded by a fog of darkness.

The villain is much lighter-heeled than I.
I followed fast, but faster he did fly,
That fallen am I in dark uneven way,
And here will rest me.

That scum is much quicker than I am. I followed fast, but he was even faster. I've ended up getting lost in the dark. I'll stop and rest here.

Thou mock'st me...
Go thy way. Faintness constraineth me
To measure out my length on this cold bed.
By day's approach look to be visited.

You're making fun of me! Go, then. I'm so tired I've got to lie down on the cold ground - but when morning is here I'll come to find you!

Lysander falls asleep.

Demetrius falls asleep.

39

First Helena, then Hermia arrives in the part of the wood where the men sleep.

O weary night, O long and tedious night,
Abate thy hours! Shine comforts from
  the east,
That I may back to Athens by daylight,
From these that my poor company
  detest;
And sleep, that sometimes shuts up
  sorrow's eye,
Steal me awhile from mine own company.

What a long, never-ending night! I wish
it were over and that the sun would
rise. Then I could return to Athens in
daylight and get away from those that
hate me. I wish sleep, that takes away
our cares, would give me some peace.

Never so weary, never so in woe;
Bedabbled with the dew and torn
  with briers,
I can no further crawl, no further go;
My legs can keep no pace with my
  desires.
Here will I rest me till the break
  of day.
Heaven shield Lysander, if they
  mean a fray!

I've never felt so tired or sad! I'm
wet with dew and scratched by
thorns. I can't drag myself further.
My legs won't do what I tell them.
I'll rest here until dawn. God keep
Lysander safe, if he gets into a fight!

Helena falls asleep.

Hermia falls asleep.

Puck arrives to dab the magic juice on
Lysander's eyes.

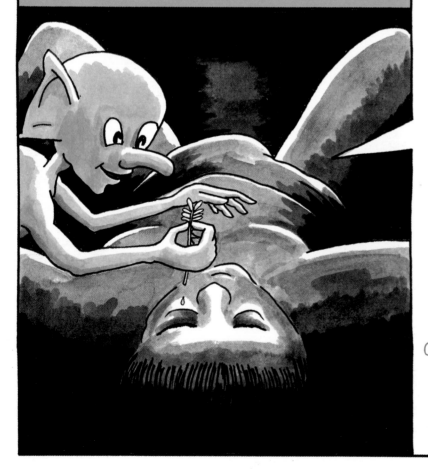

On the ground
Sleep sound:
I'll apply
To your eye,
Gentle lover, remedy.
When thou wak'st
Thou tak'st
True delight
In the sight
Of thy former lady's eye:

Sleep sound
On the ground.
The magic herb
I will apply
To your eye.
When you wake
You will take
Full delight
In the sight
Of the woman you used to love.

Jack shall have Jill;
Nought shall go ill.

Jack shall have Jill
All will be well.

The lovers are asleep near Titania and Bottom. Oberon watches all.

Come, sit thee down upon this flowery bed,
 While I thy amiable cheeks do coy,
And stick musk-roses in thy sleek smooth head,
 And kiss thy fair large ears, my gentle joy.

Come and sit down on this bed of flowers, while I stroke your lovely cheeks, stick roses in your silky hair, and kiss your beautiful, large ears, my dearest love.

Where's Peaseblossom?

Where's Peaseblossom?

Ready. I'm here.

Scratch my head, Peaseblossom... Give me your neaf, Mounsieur Mustardseed.

Scratch my head, Peaseblossom. Give me your hand to shake, Mr Mustardseed.

What's your will?

What would you like me to do?

Nothing, good Mounsieur, but to help Cavalery Cobweb to scratch. I must to the barber's, Mounsieur; for methinks I am marvail's hairy about the face; and I am such a tender ass, if my hair do but tickle me, I must scratch.

Nothing, kind sir, but to help Mr Cobweb to scratch. I must go to the barber's, sir, for I seem to have grown very hairy about the face - and I'm so soft, if a hair even tickles me, I have to scratch.

Say, sweet love, what thou desirest to eat.

Tell me what you'd like to eat, my love.

41

Truly, a peck of provender. I could munch your good dry oats. Methinks I have a great desire to a bottle of hay. Good hay, sweet hay, hath no fellow... But, I pray you, let none of your people stir me: I have an exposition of sleep come upon me.

I'd love a bit of food. I could eat some good dry oats. I really feel like eating a bottle of hay. There's nothing like good hay. But I beg you not to let anyone disturb me, as I suddenly feel very sleepy.

Sleep thou, and I will wind thee in my arms.
Fairies be gone, and be all ways away.
So doth the woodbine the sweet
   honeysuckle
Gently entwist; the female ivy so
Enrings the barky fingers of the elm.
O, how I love thee! How I dote on thee!

You sleep, and I will wrap you in my arms. Leave us, fairies. Fly off in all directions... I'll curl round you the way one flower does another; gently twist around you the way ivy rings an old elm's branches.
How I love you! How I worship you!

Welcome, good Robin. See'st thou this sweet sight?
Her dotage now I do begin to pity:
For, meeting her of late behind the wood,
Seeking sweet favours for this hateful fool,
I did upbraid her, and fall out with her...

Welcome, Robin. Have you seen this? I've begun to
feel sorry for her, in her madness. I met her not long
ago near the wood, as she was looking for things to
please this horrible fool. I told her off and teased her.

When I had at my pleasure taunted her,
And she in mild terms begged my patience,
I then did ask of her her changeling child;
Which straight she gave me, and her fairy sent
To bear him to my bower in Fairyland.
And now I have the boy, I will undo
This hateful imperfection of her eyes;
And, gentle Puck, take this transformed scalp
From off the head of this Athenian swain,
That, he awaking when the other do,
May all to Athens back again repair,
And think no more of this night's accidents,
But as the fierce vexation of a dream.
But first I will release the Fairy Queen.

When I'd had enough of teasing her, and she'd
sweetly pleaded with me to be kind to her, I asked
her to give me the stolen child. She gave him to me
straight away and her fairy sent him to my home in
Fairyland.
  Now that I have the boy, I'll take away this horrible
false way of seeing she has. I want you, Puck, to
remove the donkey's head from the Athenian - so
that he, when he wakes with the others, can go back
to Athens. None of them will think of what's
happened tonight as anything more than an
unpleasant dream. But first I'll free Titania.

Be as thou wast wont to be;
See as thou wast wont to see.
Dian's bud o'er Cupid's flower
Hath such force and blessed power.
Now, my Titania, wake you, my sweet
  Queen.

Be as you used to be before,
See things as you used to see them.
The goddess Diana's little bud has
Far greater magic than does Cupid's flower.
Now, wake, Titania, my sweet Queen.

My Oberon, what visions have I seen!
Methought I was enamoured of an ass.

What strange
things I've
seen, Oberon.
I dreamed
I was in love
with a donkey!

There lies
your love.

Your lover is
lying over
there.

How came these things to pass?
O, how mine eyes do loathe his
visage now!   How did this happen?
I can't stand the sight of him now!

Silence awhile; Robin, take off this head.
Titania, music call; and strike more
  dead
Than common sleep of all these five
  the sense...
Sound, music! Come my Queen, take
  hands with me,
And rock the ground whereon these
  sleepers be.

Keep quiet
for a moment.
Robin, take
that ass's
head from
him. Titania,
call for music
and send
these five
sleepers
into a sleep
deeper than
death. Play,
music! Take
my hand,
Titania, and
with me
dance
around these
sleepers.

Fairy King, attend, and mark:
I do hear the morning lark.

Listen, Fairy King. I can hear the
birds of early morning sing.

Then, my Queen, in silence sad,
Trip we after night's shade.
We the globe can compass soon,
Swifter than the wandering moon.

Then, my Queen, silent and sad,
we must fly after the darkness.
We can encircle the world faster
than the moon in its orbit.

Come, my lord; and in our flight,
Tell me how it came this night,
That I sleeping here was found
With these mortals on the ground.

Come, my lord. And as we fly, tell
me how it came about that I was
found sleeping on the ground
with these humans.

Theseus and Hippolyta are out hunting. The noise of hunting horns wakes the lovers. The Duke is amazed to find them all together.

I pray you all, stand up.
I know you two are rival enemies.
How comes this gentle concord in the world,
That hatred is so far from jealousy,
To sleep by hate, and fear no enmity?

Stand up, please, all of you. I know you two are enemies. How is it that with all the hatred and jealousy between you, you can sleep side by side without fear?

My lord, I shall reply amazedly,
Half sleep, half waking: but as yet, I swear,
I cannot truly say how I came here.
But, as I think (for truly would I speak),
And now I do bethink me, so it is -
I came with Hermia hither.

My lord, my reply is certain to be confused, as I'm only half awake. To be honest, I can't really say how we came to be here. But thinking about it (and I really want to be truthful), as far as I can remember - yes, that's it! - I came here with Hermia.

Enough, enough, my lord; you have enough -
I beg the law, the law upon his head!
They would have stolen away, they would, Demetrius!
Thereby to have defeated you and me,
You of your wife, and me of my consent,
Of my consent that she should be your wife.

That's enough! My lord, you've heard enough - I ask you have him put to death! They were running away, Demetrius, to get the better of both of us - cheating you of your wife and me of my wish that Hermia should marry you.

Before Theseus can reply to Egeus, Demetrius takes up the story.

My lord, fair Helen told me of their stealth,
Of this their purpose hither to this wood,
And I in fury hither followed them,
Fair Helena in fancy following me.

My lord, Helena had told me they'd run away in secret, and why they'd come to the wood. Raging with anger, I followed them here, and because of her love for me, Helena followed me.

But, my good lord, I wot not by what power -
But by some power it is - my love to Hermia,
Melted as the snow, seems to me now
As the remembrance of an idle gaud,
Which in my childhood I did dote upon;
And all the faith, the virtue of my heart,
The object and the pleasure of mine eye,
Is only Helena.

But, my lord, I don't know how, but as if by magic, my love for Hermia melted away like snow. It means no more to me now than the memory of a useless toy that I loved when I was a child. Now Helena has all my love. She's the only one I have eyes for.

Egeus, I will overbear your will;
For in the temple, by and by, with us
These couples shall be eternally knit...
Away with us to Athens.

I'm not going to do as you ask, Egeus, because quite soon these couples shall be married with us in the temple. Follow us - we're off to Athens!

Theseus and his followers leave.

Are you sure
That we are awake? It seems to me
That yet we sleep, we dream. Do not you think
The Duke was here, and bid us follow him?

Are you sure that we're awake? It feels as if we're still asleep and dreaming. Did you think the Duke was here and that he told us to follow him?

Yea, and my father.
Yes, my father was here, too.

And Hippolyta.
And Hippolyta.

And he did bid us follow.
And he did tell us to follow him.

Why, then, we are awake. Let's follow him,
And by the way let us recount our dreams.

Well, then, we must be awake. Let's follow him. On the way we can tell each other our dreams.

After the lovers have left, Bottom wakes up.

I have had a most rare vision. I have had a dream, past the wit of man to say what dream it was... The eye of man hath not heard, the ear of man hath not seen, man's hand is not able to taste, his tongue to conceive, nor his heart to report, what my dream was. I will get Peter Quince to write a ballet of this dream. It shall be called 'Bottom's Dream' because it hath no bottom; and I will sing it in the latter end of a play, before the Duke.

I've seen the most amazing things. I've had a dream, beyond the power of anyone to say what it was about. No one's eyes have ever heard, nobody's ears ever seen, anyone's hand been able to taste, no tongue ever been able to think or heart to speak about a dream such as mine. I will get Peter Quince to write a song about this dream. It shall be called 'Bottom's Dream' because it makes no sense, and I will sing it at the end of the play for the Duke.

Act 4 Scene 2

The actors are afraid Bottom won't be in time for the play - when he arrives!

Bottom! O most courageous day! O most happy hour!

Bottom's here! Wonderful! Thank goodness!

Masters, I am to discourse wonders: but ask me not what; for if I tell you, I am not true Athenian. I will tell you everything, right as it fell out.

I've got something incredible to tell you, my friends, but don't ask me what, for if I were to tell you, I wouldn't be a true Athenian. Alright, I'll tell you everything just as it happened.

Let us hear, sweet Bottom.

Let's hear it, Bottom.

Not a word of me. All that I will tell you is, that the Duke hath dined. Get your apparel... meet presently at the palace, every man look o'er his part. For the long and the short is, our play is preferred... let Thisbe have clean linen... And, most dear actors, eat no onions nor garlic, for we are to utter sweet breath, and I do not doubt but to hear them say it is a sweet comedy. No more words. Away!

I'm not saying a word. All I'll tell you is that the Duke has finished his meal. Get your things and meet up shortly at the palace. Every man study his part - for the fact is our play has been chosen! Make sure Thisbe has clean clothes. Above all, don't eat any onions or garlic, for our breath must be sweet. I'm sure they'll say it's a very sweet comedy. No more words. Action!

Act 5 Scene 1

It is evening in Athens. Theseus and Hippolyta are now married.

'Tis strange, my Theseus, that these lovers speak of.

What those lovers told us was all very strange, Theseus.

More strange than true. I never may believe
These antique fables, nor these fairy toys.
Lovers and madmen have such seething brains,
Such shaping fantasies, that apprehend
More than cool reason ever comprehends.
The lunatic, the lover and the poet
Are of imagination all compact.
One sees more devils than vast hell can hold;
That is the madman. The lover, all as frantic
Sees Helen's beauty in a brow of Egypt.

The stories were strange, for sure, but I don't think they're true. I never believe old tales or stories about fairies. Lovers and madmen have such overheated brains, they imagine things that cooler heads would never accept.

Lunatics, lovers and poets all share the same fantasies. One sees more devils than could ever exist in hell - that's the madman. The lover, as much out of control, sees gorgeous beauty in an ugly face.

The poet's eye, in a fine frenzy rolling,
Doth glance from heaven to earth, from earth to heaven;
And as imagination bodies forth
The forms of things unknown, the poet's pen
Turns them to shapes, and gives to airy nothing
A local habitation and a name.
Such tricks hath strong imagination,
That, if it would but apprehend some joy,
It comprehends some bringer of that joy;
Or in the night, imagining some fear,
How easy is a bush supposed a bear?

The poet's eye, rolling wildly about, sweeps from heaven to earth and earth to heaven. And as fast as his imagination creates new ideas, his pen shapes them - giving names and identities to things that don't exist.

That's how a strong imagination works. If it feels joy, it tells itself that something, somewhere brought that joy. Or at night, with a mind full of fears, it's easy to think that what's only a bush is actually a bear!

But all the story of the night told over,
And all their minds transfigured so together,
More witnesseth than fancy's images,
And grows to something of great constancy;
But howsoever, strange and admirable.

But having heard each lover's story of what happened last night, they all appear to agree. That suggests it was more than just a fantasy, but actually true - however strange or unlikely that may seem.

The four lovers arrive and Theseus calls Philostrate to find out what entertainments have been arranged.

Say, what abridgment have you for this evening?
What masque? What music? How shall we beguile
The lazy time, if not with some delight?

Tell me what you have to pass the time this evening. What play? What music? How shall we spend our spare time, if not with something pleasant?

There is a brief how many sports are ripe:
Make choice of which your Highness will see first.

Here is a list of the entertainments ready for you. Please choose which you'd like to see first.

Theseus reads through the list of acts, but doesn't like any of them. Then he comes across the play about Pyramus and Thisbe.

'A tedious brief scene of young Pyramus
And his love Thisbe; very tragical mirth.'
Merry and tragical? Tedious and brief?
This is hot ice and wondrous strange snow!
How shall we find the concord of this discord?

'An over-long, short play about Pyramus and his love Thisbe: a very funny tragedy.'
Funny and tragic? Long and short? This is like hot ice or snow in midsummer! Is it possible to find sanity in this insanity?

A play there is, my lord, some ten words long,
Which is as brief as I have known a play:
But by ten words, my lord, it is too long,
Which makes it tedious. For in all the play
There is not one word apt, one player fitted.
And tragical, my noble lord, it is,
For Pyramus doth therein kill himself.
Which, when I saw rehearsed, I must confess,
Made mine eyes water; but more merry tears
The passion of loud laughter never shed.

The play, my lord, is about ten words long -
which is as short a play as I've come across,
but that's still ten words too many, making it
way too long. There's not a single good word
in the play, or one actor suited to his part.
  It's called a tragedy, my lord, in that Pyramus
kills himself. And when I saw the play in
rehearsal, I have to say I cried - but no-one
has ever cried tears of such helpless laughter.

We will hear it.
    We'll have it.

No, my noble lord;
It is not for you. I have heard it over,
And it is nothing, nothing in the world;
Unless you can find sport in their intents,
Extremely stretched, and conned with
   cruel pain,
To do you service.

No, my lord, it's not for you. I've heard it
read and it's useless, complete rubbish -
unless you find funny all the hard work
they've put into the play to please you.

I will hear that play;
For never anything can be amiss,
When simpleness and duty tender it.
Go, bring them in.

I'll watch that
play. For
nothing can
ever be too
bad, when
done
without fuss
and a wish
to please.
Go and
fetch them.

Philostrate leaves to find the actors.

I love not to see wretchedness
   o'ercharged,
And duty in his service perishing.

I hate to see people made fools of,
when they're trying to do their best.

Why, gentle sweet,
   you shall see
   no such thing.

Why, my love,
   you'll see no
   such thing.

He says they can do nothing in this kind.

He says they're hopeless.

The kinder we, to give them thanks for nothing. Our sport shall be to take what they mistake; And what poor duty cannot do, noble respect Takes it in might, not merit.

That makes us all the kinder, then, for thanking them for nothing. We'll enjoy what they attempt, even if they mess it up. And if it's awful, despite their wish to please, we'll respect their efforts.

Peter Quince arrives with the introduction.

If we offend, it is with our good will.
    That you should think, we come not to offend,
But with good will. To show our simple skill,
    That is the true beginning of our end.
Consider, then, we come but in despite.
    We do not come, as minding to content you,
Our true intent is. All for your delight,
    We are not here. That you should here repent you,
The actors are at hand; and, by their show,
You shall know all, that you are like to know.

If we upset you, we mean to. To tell you that we don't want to upset, but please you. All we really want to do, is show off. To show off our simple skills. We're here to cause pain. We haven't come to please you. What we want to do is. For your pleasure, we are not here. That you should take pity on yourselves, because the actors are now here. You'll find out all you need to know about the play.

This fellow doth not stand upon points.

This man doesn't have any idea about full stops.

He hath rid his prologue like a rough colt; he knows not the stop.

He's read through his introduction like a man on a wild young horse - he doesn't have any control.

Gentles, perchance you wonder at this show;
  But wonder on, till truth make all things plain.
This man is Pyramus, if you would know;
  This beauteous lady Thisbe is certain.
This man, with lime and roughcast, doth present
  Wall, that vile wall which did these lovers
  sunder;
And through Wall's chink, poor souls, they
  are content
  To whisper. At the which let no man wonder.
This man, with lanthorn, dog, and bush of thorn,
  Presenteth Moonshine; for, if you will know,
By moonshine did these lovers think no scorn
  To meet at Ninus' tomb, there, there to woo.
This grisly beast, which Lion hight by name,
The trusty Thisbe, coming first by night,
Did scare away, or rather did affright;
And, as she fled, her mantle she did fall,
  Which Lion vile with bloody mouth did stain.
Anon comes Pyramus, sweet youth and tall,
  And finds his trusty Thisbe's mantle slain:
Whereat, with blade, with bloody blameful blade,
  He bravely broached his boiling bloody breast;
And Thisbe, tarrying in mulberry shade,
  His dagger drew, and died. For all the rest,
Let Lion, Moonshine, Wall, and lovers twain
  At large discourse, while here they do remain.

It maybe you're wondering what this show's about - but keep guessing until all's been explained. This man is Pyramus, and this beautiful lady is Thisbe. This man, covered in plaster stands for the wall - that horrible wall that kept the lovers apart. All they can do is whisper to each other through a hole in the wall. Which shouldn't surprise anyone. This man, with the lantern, dog and thorn bush is the moon - for it was by moonlight that the two lovers were brave enough to meet one another at a tomb. This frightening animal, called Lion, scared Thisbe (who arrived first, at night). As she ran away, she dropped her shawl, which the lion stained with its bloody mouth. Pyramus, a tall, sweet young man, comes along later. He finds Thisbe's bloody shawl, and thinking her dead, bravely kills himself with a blade to his bloody breast. Thisbe had been waiting in a wood. On Pyramus' death, she takes his knife and stabs herself to death. Let Lion, Moonshine, Wall and the two lovers tell you the rest, while here on stage.

I wonder if the lion be to
  speak?

I wonder if the lion gets
to say anything?

No wonder, my lord. One lion
  may, when many asses do.

Don't be surprised if it does,
my lord. Why shouldn't one
lion speak, when so many
asses do?

The play begins. Flute is wearing a mask.

O wall, full often hast thou heard my moans,
  For parting my fair Pyramus and me!
My cherry lips have often kissed thy stones,
  Thy stones with lime and hair knit up in thee.

O wall, you've often heard me complain at you for keeping me from my love, Pyramus. My red lips have often kissed your stones - stones held together with lime and hair.

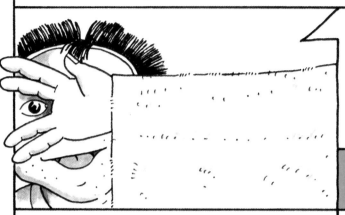

I see a voice; now will I to the chink,
To spy and I can hear my Thisbe's face.
Thisbe!

I see a voice. I'll go to the gap in the wall and look through, so I can hear Thisbe's face. Thisbe!

Bottom looks through a gap in the wall made by Snout's two fingers.

My love thou art, my love I think.

My love? You are my love, I think.

O, kiss me through the hole of this vile wall!

Kiss me through the hole in this horrible wall.

Think what thou wilt, I am thy lover's grace.

You can think what you like. I am your lover.

I kiss the wall's hole, not your lips at all.

I'm kissing the wall's hole, not your lips!

Wilt thou at Ninny's tomb meet me straightway?

Will you meet me right now at Ninny's tomb?

Thus have I, Wall, my part discharged so;
And, being done, thus Wall away doth go.

As Wall, I've finished my part in the play, so I'm off.

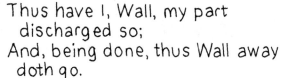

'Tide life, 'tide death, I come without delay.

Alive or dead, I'll go there immediately.

This is the silliest stuff that ever I heard.

This is the silliest stuff I ever heard.

The best in this kind are but shadows; and the worst are no worse, if imagination amend them.

The best actors are only shadows of real life, and the worst are not worse than those, if they're helped out with some imagination.

It must be your imagination then, and not theirs.

Then it will have to be your imagination, not theirs - they haven't any.

If we imagine no worse of them than they of themselves, they may pass for excellent men.

If we think of them as well as they think of themselves, they'll be excellent.

You, ladies, you whose gentle hearts do fear
The smallest monstrous mouse that creeps on floor,
May now perchance both quake and tremble here,
When Lion rough in wildest rage doth roar.
Then know that I, as Snug the joiner, am
A lion fell, nor else no lion's dam;
For, if I should as lion come in strife
Into this place, 'twere pity on my life.

Ladies - you whose faint hearts are afraid of the smallest giant mouse creeping on the floor, may perhaps be frightened at this point, when the rough lion roars in wild rage. So you should know that it's me, Snug the carpenter, playing a lion (not its wife). I'm not a real lion, for it would be very wrong of me to come here as a real one.

54

All that I have to say is to tell you that the lanthorn is the moon; I, the man i' th' moon; this thorn bush, my thorn bush; and this dog, my dog.

All I have to say is to tell you that this lantern is the moon, and that I am the man in the moon. This thorn bush is my thorn bush, and this dog is my dog.

Why, all these should be in the lanthorn; for all these are in the moon. But silence! Here comes Thisbe.

Why, they should all be in the lantern, for they're all in the moon. But silence! Here comes Thisbe.

As Thisbe enters, the lion roars. She runs off stage, but leaving her shawl.

Oh! Ohh!

Well roared, Lion!
Good roaring, Lion!

Well run, Thisbe!
Good running, Thisbe!

Well shone, Moon! Truly, the moon shines with a good grace.
Good shining, Moon. It has to be said, the moon shines very well.

55

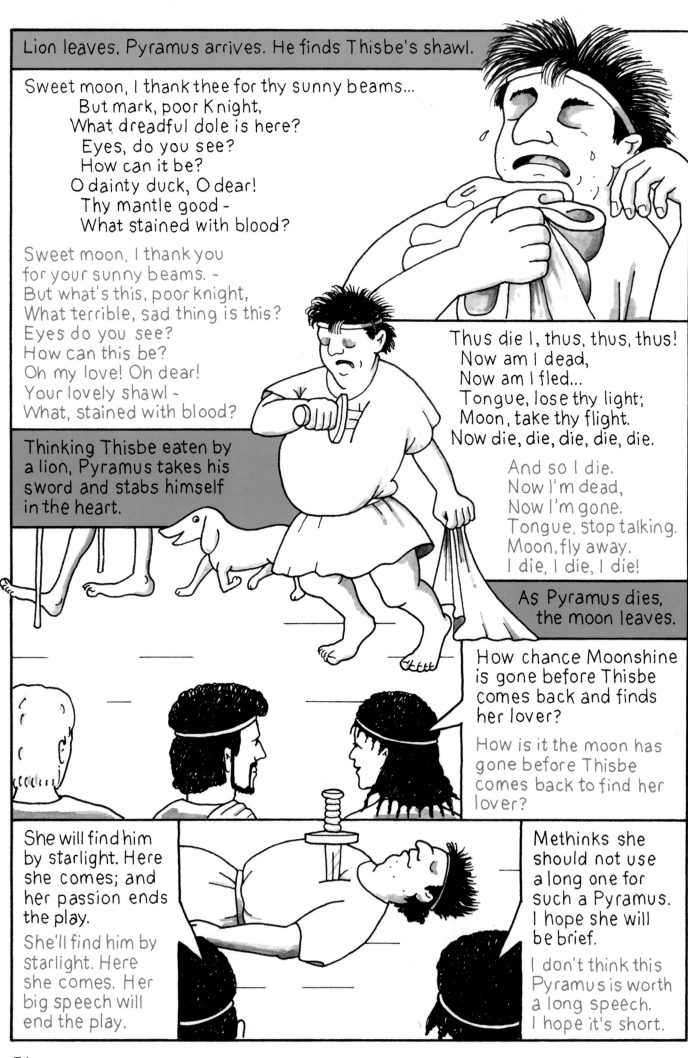

Lion leaves. Pyramus arrives. He finds Thisbe's shawl.

Sweet moon, I thank thee for thy sunny beams...
But mark, poor Knight,
What dreadful dole is here?
Eyes, do you see?
How can it be?
O dainty duck, O dear!
Thy mantle good -
What stained with blood?

Sweet moon, I thank you
for your sunny beams. -
But what's this, poor knight,
What terrible, sad thing is this?
Eyes do you see?
How can this be?
Oh my love! Oh dear!
Your lovely shawl -
What, stained with blood?

Thinking Thisbe eaten by a lion, Pyramus takes his sword and stabs himself in the heart.

Thus die I, thus, thus, thus!
Now am I dead,
Now am I fled...
Tongue, lose thy light;
Moon, take thy flight.
Now die, die, die, die, die.

And so I die.
Now I'm dead,
Now I'm gone.
Tongue, stop talking.
Moon, fly away.
I die, I die, I die!

As Pyramus dies, the moon leaves.

How chance Moonshine is gone before Thisbe comes back and finds her lover?

How is it the moon has gone before Thisbe comes back to find her lover?

She will find him by starlight. Here she comes; and her passion ends the play.

She'll find him by starlight. Here she comes. Her big speech will end the play.

Methinks she should not use a long one for such a Pyramus. I hope she will be brief.

I don't think this Pyramus is worth a long speech. I hope it's short.

Thisbe finds Pyramus.

Dead, dead? A tomb
Must cover thy sweet eyes.
  These lily lips,
  This cherry nose,
These yellow cowslip cheeks,
  Are gone, are gone.
  Lovers, make moan.
His eyes were green as leeks.
  O Sisters Three,
  Come, come to me,
With hands as pale as milk;
  Lay them in gore,
  Since you have shore
With shears his thread of silk.

Dead? Dead? A tomb
Must cover your sweet eyes.
Your white lips,
Your red nose,
Your bright yellow cheeks,
Are gone, are gone.
Lovers cry out.
His eyes were as green
  as leeks.
Sisters of Death
Come to me,
Lay your milky white hands
In his blood,
Since it's you who have cut
The silk thread of his life
  with your scissors.

  Tongue, not a word.
  Come, trusty sword.
Come, blade, my breast
  imbrue!
  And farewell, friends.
  Thus Thisbe ends.
Adieu, adieu, adieu.

No more words.
Come, my good sword.
Come, blade -
Stab my breast.
Goodbye, my friends.
My life is at an end.
Goodbye, goodbye.

Moonshine and Lion
are left to bury the dead.

Only Moonshine and
Lion are left to bury
the dead.

Aye, and Wall too.

And there's Wall too.

No, I assure you; the
wall is down that parted
their fathers. Will it
please you to see the
epilogue, or to hear a
Bergomask dance
between two of our
company?

No, you're quite wrong. The wall that kept their
fathers apart has been pulled down. Would you like
to see a few last words, or hear a country dance put
on by two of us?

No epilogue, I pray you; for your play needs no excuse. Never excuse; for when the players are all dead, there need none to be blamed. Marry, if he that writ it had played Pyramus and hanged himself in Thisbe's garter, it would have been a fine tragedy: and so it is truly, and very notably discharged... Let your epilogue alone.

No closing words, please, for your play needs no apologies - when all the actors are dead, there's no-one left to blame anyway. If the writer of it had also played Pyramus and then hanged himself with Thisbe's garter, that would have been a fine tragedy - as of course it was. And very well acted - so don't worry about final words.

The iron tongue of midnight hath told
  twelve.
Lovers, to bed; 'tis almost fairy time.
I fear we shall outsleep the coming
  morn,
As much as we this night have
  overwatched.
This palpable-gross play hath well
  beguiled
The heavy gait of night. Sweet friends,
  to bed.

That bell tells us it's midnight. Lovers, to bed - the night will soon belong to the fairies. I'm afraid we'll oversleep in the morning by the same length of time we stayed up too late. This ridiculous play made us forget what time it was. Good friends, it's bedtime.

After everyone has left, Puck arrives.

Now the hungry lion roars,
  And the wolf behowls the moon;
Whilst the heavy ploughman snores,
  All with weary task fordone.
Now the wasted brands do glow,
  Whilst the screech-owl, screeching loud,
Puts the wretch that lies in woe
  In remembrance of a shroud.

The hungry lion is roaring,
As the wolf howls at the moon
And the tired farm-worker snores,
Exhausted by his hard work.
The fire is almost burnt out,
While the loud cries of the barn owl
Force those who lie in beds of pain
To think about their coming death.

Now it is the time of night,
  That the graves all gaping wide,
Every one lets forth his sprite,
  In the church-way paths to glide.
And we fairies, that do run
  By the triple Hecate's team,
From the presence of the sun,
  Following darkness like a dream,
Now are frolic; not a mouse
Shall disturb this hallowed house:
I am sent, with broom, before,
To sweep the dust behind the door.

Now is the time of night
When graves open wide
And each sets free a ghost,
To glide about the churchyard paths.
And we fairies that serve the three
  moon goddesses, hide from daylight
And follow darkness as in a dream,
Are in our playtime. Not even a mouse
Shall disturb this special house,
I've been sent on ahead with a broom,
To sweep all the dust behind the door.

Oberon and Titania arrive with all their followers.

Now, until the break of day,
Through this house each fairy stray.
To the best bride-bed will we,
Which by us shall blessed be.

Between now and morning,
Every fairy must wander through this
  house.
I shall go to the marriage bed and
  give it my blessing.

With this field-dew consecrate,
Every fairy take his gait,
And each several chamber bless,
Through this palace, with sweet peace;
And the owner of it blest
Ever shall in safety rest.
Trip away; make no stay;
Meet me all by break of day.

Every one of you fairies must get busy.
Each must take some of the magic
  dew-drops
And should use it to bless each room
  with peace,
So that its owner, protected in this way,
Shall always live safe from harm.
Don't wait - be off.
Make sure you all meet me at daybreak.

Oberon, Titania and the fairies all leave. Puck is alone.

If we shadows have offended,
Think but this, and all is mended:
That you have but slumb'red here,
While these visions did appear.
And this weak and idle theme,
No more yielding but a dream,
Gentles, do not reprehend:
If you pardon, we will mend.
And, as I am an honest Puck,
If we have unearned luck
Now to 'scape the serpent's tongue,
We will make amends ere long;
Else the Puck a liar call.
So, good night unto you all.
Give me your hands, if we be friends,
And Robin shall restore amends.

If you've been upset by any of us in
  this play,
Just think of this and all will be well again:
You've simply been asleep while here,
As strange sights passed before your
  eyes.
This whole weak, time-wasting show,
Means no more than any dream.
So please don't blame us, good people.
If you forgive us for this, we'll try
  harder in future.
And, as I'm an honest person,
If we have the good fortune
To escape your boos and hisses now,
We'll make sure we do better next time -
Or call me a liar.
So, goodnight to you all.
Clap your hands, if we are friends,
And I'll return the favour another time!

The end.